Topic 1
Absolute and relative morality

Cognitivism and non-cognitivism

Philosophers fall into one of two broad categories. The first group believes that there are **moral facts**, i.e. that moral language refers to actual and distinct qualities. If there are **objective** moral facts, then they can be tested and they make a difference to the thing they describe. This way of thinking is called **cognitivism**. The second group believes that there are no moral facts. Ethics do not describe objective qualities but subjective moods, attitudes and actions. This way of thinking is called **non-cognitivism**.

An essential distinction that must be tested in ethical discussion was made by the eighteenth-century philosopher **David Hume**. Hume noticed that people often argue from objective statements about the world and from these infer moral **value judgements**. Hume argued that this is a false move and treats moral facts as if they are in the same class as physical or empirical facts. The principle of 'Hume's Fork' argues that this is not so: you cannot *logically* derive an 'ought' (value judgement) from an 'is' (fact statement). This is the facts-value distinction; Hume's Fork is often termed the **naturalistic fallacy** today.

In the twentieth century the most extreme subjectivist non-cognitive ethical idea ('emotivism') was presented by **A. J. Ayer**. Ayer argued that good/bad are literally 'non-sense' words. This is because, for something to be meaningful, it has either to be logically true ('analytical truth') or empirically true ('synthetic truth'). Good/bad are just subjective exclamations and have no meaning.

Moral relativism

The term 'moral relativism' has a wide range of meanings. Many use it to refer to all subjective theories of ethics where humans decide what is right or wrong, referring to **Protagoras'** (485–420 BCE) famous saying, 'Man is the measure of all things'. This is reinforced by the observation of **cultural relativists** that different cultures do things very differently because they have different values, which gain authority only because they are passed on as important traditions. The ancient historian Herodotus famously concluded that 'custom is king of all'.

Normative moral relativists argue that moral relativism is not just an observation but a moral system (just like utilitarianism). Some argue (cognitive moral relativists) that there may be one or two very basic human values that every culture and age interprets differently. One example might be 'respect for property': J. S. Mill argued for respect of personal autonomy; Joseph Fletcher claimed it was love (or *agape*). Tolerance is often considered a key characteristic of normative moral relativism — but how much should one tolerate?

The moral **objectivist** believes that there are some values that are **intrinsically** right and wrong; these are not open to negotiation. This is an **absolute** objective position. Plato's 'Good', for example, is the basis of justice. But in practice even objective systems have subjective elements. Aquinas' natural law appears to have five objective primary precepts but these have to be interpreted according to situation. The Bible may be a witness to God's commands (absolute and objective) but these commands often appear to contradict each other and are reinterpreted according to new situations and circumstances (notably Jesus' adjustments to the Torah).

1 Explain the difference between cognitive and non-cognitive ethics.

....

....

....

2 How is Hume's Fork significant for moral subjectivism?

....

....

....

....

3 Complete Hume's saying:

'Morality is more p .... f .... than j ....'

4 What does 'extrinsic value' mean?

....

....

....

5 A. J. Ayer offers a radical non-cognitive subjective view of ethics. Explain why he claimed that moral statements are neither analytically true, nor synthetically true, but 'emotive'.

....

....

....

....

6 Complete Protagoras' saying:

'Man is the m .... of a .... things.'

7 What point was Herodotus making when he concluded 'custom is king of all'?

....

....

....

....

8 How is the 'diversity thesis' used by some moral relativists?

....

....

....

....

9 What is 'normative cognitive moral relativism'?

....

....

....

10 Why might a cognitive moral relativist condemn female circumcision?

....

....

....

....

11 Give a definition of moral absolutism.

....

....

....

....

12 Explain why each of the following could be said to hold a moral absolutist and objective view of morality.

Human rights ....

....

....

God/revealed ethics (Bible etc.) ....

....

....

....

Plato ....

....

....

....

Natural law ....

....

....

....

13 Give two problems with absolute ethics.

....

....

....

....

....

14 What does 'intrinsic value' mean?

....

....

15 What does deontological mean?

....

....

....

....

16 Give two examples of deontological normative ethical systems.

....

....

....

....

17 What does teleological mean?

....

....

Exam-style question

Answer the following part questions on a separate sheet of paper. Allow 25 minutes for Part a and 15 minutes for Part b. Use 2 minutes to plan and 2 minutes to reread your essay and correct mistakes.

a Explain what is meant when it is said that ethics are objective and absolute.   `25 marks` `25`

b 'There are no moral absolutes because no one agrees what they are.' Discuss.   `10 marks` `15`

Topic 2
Natural law

What is natural law?

Natural law ethicists consider that there are some values that are **intrinsically** right and wrong and these are **objective** and **cognitive**. The attractiveness of natural law is (in theory) that it is universal, prescriptive, consistent, rational and social. It exists in religious and non-religious forms. The non-religious form was developed by Aristotle and then adapted theologically by **Aquinas** (*c*.1224–1274). Natural law is the basis of many forms of Christian ethics, especially Roman Catholicism.

Aquinas argued that all things are created with a distinctive purpose or **telos**. When human beings fully achieve their purpose, they can be said to be happy, flourishing or perfect. This is the state of *eudaimonia*. As God is the efficient cause of nature, then (as suggested in Genesis 1) the purpose of human existence is to live according to God's purpose in nature by 'doing good and avoiding evil'. Aquinas agreed with Cicero's notion that, 'True law is right reason in agreement with nature'. Reason is therefore able to reject those desires that are not part of God-given human nature. Reason discerns five **primary precepts**: preserve innocent life, live in ordered societies, worship God, educate children, reproduce. From these precepts each society is able to develop its own **secondary precepts**. So, for example, marriage is derived from the primary precept of reproduction, the need to educate the young and establish ordered society. However, for Christians, marriage is reinforced through another aspect of God's **divine law**, the **revealed law** of the Bible.

Subjectivity

Aquinas therefore shows that, even in an objective moral system, subjectivity is necessary. Every act requires the right intention or **interior act** as well as compliance with the law itself (**exterior act**) and this will depend sometimes, in the absence of clear guidance, on conscience and developing a good character through the **virtues**. This sometimes leads to an **apparent good** where, either through faulty reason or a weak interior act, a person (or society) fails to achieve perfection.

A good example of subjectivity in natural law is the **doctrine of double effect** (DDE). The DDE states that an action is good if the primary intention is good even if there is an indirect bad consequence, providing this consequence is not disproportionately evil compared to the good end. So, giving a dying woman pain relief (good end) even though this might foreshorten her life (unwilled indirect result), is permissible.

Weaknesses of natural law

The main weakness of natural law is not being able to determine what is meant by nature or natural. It should be clear that nature does not mean what happens in nature or among animals, as their purposes are different from humans. Another problem is that many things have several purposes. For example, what is sex for — procreation, love, pleasure? Do all three have to be fulfilled at the same time or can they be separated? Many accuse natural law, and especially the DDE, of **casuistry** — used negatively to mean the use of clever arguments to get round a legal problem. Utilitarians consider the DDE to be a confused form of consequentialism. The fundamental problem is that all forms of natural law suffer from the **naturalistic fallacy** (see Topic 1).

1 Complete the following saying (Cicero *De Republica* III):

'True l................................. is right r................................. in agreement with n..................................'

2 Outline Aristotle's main characteristics of non-religious natural law.

....

....

....

....

3 The fundamental natural law principle is:

'G................................. is to be d................................. and pursued, e................................. is to be a.................................'

4 Aquinas argues that, as God is the first and final cause of nature, then the five *primary* purposes/precepts of human life in doing good and avoiding evil are (*tick five*):

☐ to reproduce

☐ to live in ordered society

☐ to be happy

☐ to become autonomous

☐ to preserve life

☐ to worship God as the source of goodness

☐ to become a ruler

☐ to be beautiful

☐ to live by reason and educate children

☐ to become important

5 Revealed law is (*tick correct statements*):

☐ natural law from before the creation

☐ a super rational law

☐ laws given to compensate for human frailty

☐ special laws revealed in the Bible

☐ laws for life after death

☐ God's special revelation which is not contrary to natural law

6 What are interior acts? Give an example.

....

....

....

7 Name some of the virtues that Aquinas considered to be the basis of interior acts.

....

....

....

....

8 What is the relationship between interior acts and exterior acts?

9 Aquinas allows that natural law may well appear situational and differ from place to place. He explains this through primary and secondary principles. What does he mean?

10 Outline Aquinas' reasoning (using primary and secondary precepts) why sex must be within heterosexual marriage and procreative.

11 Aquinas argues that even those acting according to natural law will come to different conclusions. Often this is due to what he calls 'apparent goods'. What is an apparent good?

12 Give two examples of an apparent good.

13 A major principle that gives natural law some element of 'situationism' is the doctrine of double effect (DDE). Explain this in terms of acts, intentions and effects (proportion).

....

....

....

....

....

14 Explain the following weaknesses of natural law:

lack of telos (Darwin) ....

....

....

....

....

several purposes ....

....

....

....

....

failings of human reason (problem of sin) ....

....

....

....

....

naturalistic fallacy ....

....

....

....

....

casuistry and cruelty ....

....

....

....

....

15 **Explain the following strengths of natural law:**

human rights ....
....
....

agent centred and action centred ....
....
....
....
....

sense solidarity with all humans ....
....
....
....

fairness ....
....
....
....

Exam-style question

Answer the following part questions on a separate sheet of paper. Allow 25 minutes for Part a and 15 minutes for Part b. Use 2 minutes to plan and 2 minutes to reread your essay and correct mistakes.

a Explain Aquinas' teaching on purpose and perfection in natural law. `25 marks` (25)

b Assess the view that natural law is out of date. `10 marks` (15)

Topic 3
Kantian ethics

The hypothetical and categorical imperative

Kant's ethics are strongly **deontological** (duty based). However, he did not believe duties are natural or revealed but the result of a **good will** which all humans possess. The good will exists a priori; he did not prove its existence. He also argued that we have the freedom to act according to our good will if we act rationally and not emotionally. When we decide that there are no rational contradictions to acting in a certain way, then we are truly free to act in that way. This is what he meant when he said, 'ought implies can'. To test that we are indeed acting rationally and freely according to the good will, Kant devised various tests.

The first is the universalising test or **formula of universal law**. This means distinguishing between something that looks like a duty but which is in fact merely something I desire. This he termed **hypothetical imperatives**, which are conditional on situation and feelings or **inclinations** (as Kant terms them) such as love and desires; they are often in the form 'if I want x then I ought to do y.' True duties, though, are **categorical** and are not situational but based on reason. Categorical imperatives have to imagine a state of affairs (he called it the 'kingdom of ends') where everyone is not only a rule maker but also a rule abider. In other words, I have to imagine what the world would be like if I decided to break my promise and permitted everyone else to abandon promise keeping. Kant famously said 'do your duties though the heavens fall'. A good example Kant gives of the difference between the hypothetical and the categorical imperatives is the story of the 'prudent shopkeeper'. The shopkeeper who gives the right change to customers because he gains a good reputation (and thereby increases trade) is not morally good, because he is not acting out of a universal moral duty always to be honest.

The second test or version of the categorical, sometimes called the **practical imperative** or **formula of humanity**, is that people should never be treated as a means to an end but as an end in themselves. In other words, when we will our neighbours' good we do so because they are fellow human beings. This was one reason why Kant strongly rejected utilitarianism, because it treats people as a means to an end and does not respect them as humans. The third test is to consider that, in the perfect state, the **kingdom of ends**, one is not only a lawmaker, but a law-abider.

Strengths and weaknesses of Kantian ethics

Some of the strengths of Kant are that he develops a rational system that emphasises human dignity. The universalising principle not only develops an idea of justice but of human rights: it respects individuals as autonomous decision makers responsible for their actions.

Some of the weaknesses are that he fails to deal with **clashing duties:** that is, when two equally demanding duties cannot be resolved without either using consequentialism or appealing to another, higher, law than the categorical imperative. Another problem is that he appears to prefer **reason over people**. Many argue that Kant is **counter-intuitive** and refer to the strange example he gives of providing a killer the information he needs so that he can find and kill his victim, based on the maxim that it is one's duty always to tell the truth. The **inflexibility** of moral law appears to make it more important than people. Finally, many consider Kant to give priority to the prevailing values of his own culture and time rather than independent reason. Cannibals might well consider eating their enemies a universal duty, but it is not a European tradition and would probably fail the categorical imperative test.

1 Which best describes Kant's ethics? (*tick one*)

☐ deontological, a posteriori, universal, intuitive

☐ consequential, a priori, universal, intuitive

☐ deontological, a priori, universal, rational

☐ consequential, a posteriori, metaphysical, rational

2 What fundamental point was Kant making about humans when he argued that 'ought implies can'?

3 What is the good will?

4 Complete the following quotation:

'Do your d .... though the h .... fall.'

5 Complete the following quotation:

'Good will s .... forth like a p .... j ....'

6 Complete the following quotation:

'Two things fill my mind with ever new and increasing a .... and a ....

— the s .... h .... above me and the m .... l .... within me.'

7 What is the hypothetical imperative?

8 Complete the following:

The hypothetical imperative 'is good for some p .... either p ....

or a .... '.

9 Outline Kant's example of the 'prudent shopkeeper', which he used to illustrate the hypothetical.

....

....

....

....

10 Why are hypothetical imperatives *not* moral duties according to Kant?

....

....

....

....

11 The 'formula of universal law' of the categorical imperative is to:

'Act as if the maxim of y .... a .... were to become t ....

your w .... a u .... law of nature.'

12 What is a maxim?

....

....

13 Outline the stages Kant gives for why a lying promising cannot become universal law:

the desire/proposal ....

....

....

contradiction ....

....

....

conclusion ....

....

....

14 The 'formula of humanity' version (the practical imperative) is to:

'Act in such a way that you treat h ...., whether in your own p ....

or in the p .... of another, always at the same time as an e ....

never simply as a m ....'

15 The 'formula of the kingdom of ends' is to:

'Act as if you were a l _____ m _____ and l _____ r _____

member of the Kingdom of Ends.'

16 Why does Kant criticise those who act out love for humanity (the 'friend of man')?

_____

_____

_____

_____

17 What are Kant's summmum bonum and its three postulates?

_____

_____

_____

_____

18 Two strengths of Kant's moral philosophy are:

_____

_____

_____

_____

19 Two weaknesses of Kant's moral philosophy are:

_____

_____

_____

_____

Exam-style question

Answer the following part questions on a separate sheet of paper. Allow 25 minutes for Part a and 15 minutes for Part b. Use 2 minutes to plan and 2 minutes to reread your essay and correct mistakes.

a Explain Kant's universalising principle to establish the summum bonum.

25 marks

b To what extent does Kant's ethical theory solve moral problems?

10 marks

Topic 4
Utilitarianism

What is utilitarianism?

Utilitarianism comes from the word utility, which simply means 'useful'. In its modern form, **Jeremy Bentham**, as a legal reformer, developed the notion of utility to offer a clear, rational and scientific means of deciding whether a law was good in making people happy or unhappy. However, he came also to consider that all our actions and moral values can be reduced to a single self-evident principle. As he said: 'Nature has placed mankind under the governance of two sovereign masters, pain and pleasure.' Utilitarianism rejects the idea that morality is natural, God-given or derived from a 'good will' (Kant). However, despite Bentham's very clear starting point, utilitarianism has developed in various ways. According to modern custom, utilitarianism falls broadly into three types: act, rule and preference.

Act utilitarianism

Bentham can be described as an **act utilitarian**. This is because every situation can be assessed on what will bring about the greatest happiness or pleasure and least amount of pain. Bentham was a reductionist and considered pleasure/pain to be essentially physical, so he developed a 'hedonic calculus' that estimated the quantity (how much), tendency (how often), and number (how many people would be) affected by a particular action (the 'act'). He considered all pleasures to be **homogeneous**, that is, all are extrinsically equal and entirely dependent on situation and personal preference. As a consequentialist, he considered that the ends (happiness/pleasure) justified the means (regardless of intentions).

Rule utilitarianism

Some have described **J. S. Mill** as a **rule utilitarian**, a term he never used himself, but one that suggests that he differed from Bentham in several ways. First, he believed in the 'law of tendency'. Just as nature behaves in certain predictable ways, so do humans, and so certain actions tend to produce similar effects. Mill argued that those who are skilled in these matters (he called them 'competent judges') can predict likely outcomes. Rules, therefore, are very useful in utilitarianism as they save time, treat people consistently and, based on past experience, can efficiently predict greater happiness for all in the future.

Second, Mill disagreed with Bentham that all pleasures are the same. Happiness is **heterogeneous**, and 'higher' or 'intellectual' pleasures separate humans from lower, more basic pleasures associated with the animal side of human nature. He rejected Bentham's claim that 'quantity of pleasure being equal, pushpin is as good as poetry' and called it 'pig doctrine'. What matters is the quality of happiness; he argued that 'it is better to be a human being dissatisfied than a pig satisfied; better to be Socrates dissatisfied than a fool satisfied'.

Preference utilitarianism

Preference utilitarianism is not radically different from act utilitarianism: it also seeks the greatest happiness of the greatest number but does so by taking into account the range of preferences that are relevant in any given situation. **Peter Singer** is an influential modern preference utilitarian. The advantage with this is that we do not have to ask what is happiness or what is pain but, rather, what preferences and interests are being expressed. Not all preferences are the same but they all deserve equal consideration.

Singer's two key principles of **equal consideration** and **equality of interests** widen the 'greatest number' to include non-human animals. This is because it would be irrational and therefore **speciesist** not to include non-human animals who have preferences and interests. Preferences can be arranged in hierarchy depending on how well sentience is developed. It ranges from creatures who are fully aware to those that are capable only of basic sensations of pain.

1 **What does utilitarianism mean?**

....

2 **How is utilitarianism a form of consequentialism?**

....

....

3 **Bentham said of natural rights that they were:**

'Nonsense on s ....'.

4 **Complete Bentham's statement:**

'Nature has placed mankind under the g .... of two s ....

masters, p .... and p ....'

5 **Complete Bentham's comment:**

'Quantity of p .... being e ...., p .... is as good as p ....'.

What does it mean to say that Bentham considered pleasures to be homogeneous?

....

....

....

6 **As a moral reductionist, Bentham developed a 'hedonic calculus' so as to be able to determine happiness/pleasure.**

'Hedonic' means ....

....

'Moral reductionism' means ....

....

7 The calculus may be arranged to cover three areas. Outline the seven elements of the calculus and arrange them into these three areas:

quantity ....

....

tendency ....

....

how many ....

....

8 Explain how Bentham's utilitarianism helps to reject moral taboos (such as homosexuality).

....

....

....

....

9 Give two ways in which Mill's utilitarianism is different from Bentham's utilitarianism.

....

....

....

....

....

10 Complete the following famous statement by Mill:

'It is better to be a human being d .... than a pig s .... ; better

to be m .... dissatisfied than a f .... satisfied. And if the f .... or the pig

are of different opinion it is only because they only know their side of the question. The other

party to the comparison knows b .... sides.'

11 Why does Mill consider there are 'higher pleasures'? Give two examples.

....

....

....

....

12 What is the role of Mill's 'competent judges'?

....

....

13 Why does Mill reject Kant's notion of the good will?

....

....

14 How does Mill justify acting for the good of others?

....

....

....

15 How does Mill argue for rule utilitarianism based on 'tendency' and 'secondary precepts'?

....

....

....

16 Explain why the utilitarian consequential principle of the 'ends justifying the means' might be criticised for:

being morally 'cold' or failing to treat humans as persons

....

....

....

being unjust (to minorities)

....

....

....

being unable to calculate the future precisely (the ripple effect)

....

....

....

being unable to define quantity and/or quality of happiness

....

....

....

17 Complete Singer's comment (quoting Bentham) about animals:

'The question is not can they r .... ? nor can they t .... ? but can they

s .... ?'

18 Sentience determines how morally considerable an animal is according to Singer. Explain his principle of equal consideration when applied to: human adults, newborn human babies, great apes, dolphins, rabbits, dogs, horses, flies, bacteria, rocks.

....

....

....

....

....

....

....

....

Exam-style question

Answer the following part questions on a separate sheet of paper. Allow 25 minutes for Part a and 15 minutes for Part b. Use the suggested plan, add your own notes, then turn these notes into an essay.

a Explain Peter Singer's preference utilitarianism.

25 marks (25)

- Introduction to the basic aims of all utilitarian systems
- How and in what ways preference is same/different from Bentham
- Singer's notion of sentience
- Sentience and non-human animals
- What it means to be 'morally considerable'
- Examples of how preference utilitarianism might work in practice

b 'The greatest happiness of the greatest number must include the happiness of non-human animals.' Discuss.

10 marks (15)

The case for:

- Morality is about reducing pain because...
- So, sentience must apply to human and non-human animals because...
- In which case 'the greatest number' is desirable because...
- Initial conclusion

The case against:

- Singer has made sentience too broad a concept because...
- So, if morality/rights imply reciprocal duties, then non-human animals are not included because...
- Furthermore, if judging consequences for humans is difficult then including animals makes this impossible because...

Conclusion

Topic 5
Religious ethics

Christian ethics

The OCR specification does not state which religions you are to study so you may choose one of the religions referred to elsewhere in the specification (i.e. Buddhism, Christianity, Hinduism, Islam or Judaism). Most textbooks present religious ethics from the Christian tradition.

For most Christians, the main ethical principles of Christianity depend on a combination of the Bible, reason and tradition. For more **conservative Christians**, as the Bible is regarded as a witness to God's revelation, it therefore has the greatest authority. The Old Testament establishes the notion that ethics are social and based on a **covenant** with God — the **Ten Commandments** are a summary of these two ideas. The prophets, such as Amos and Isaiah, focus in particular on social justice and the treatment of the poor as examples of the true nature of God's covenant.

In the New Testament, Jesus' **Sermon on the Mount** (Matthew 5–7) is often considered a focal point of his moral teaching; here Jesus teaches that being good is not only about keeping the Law but the **inner law** of love, righteousness, peace, faith. Christians are to be 'perfect, as your heavenly Father is perfect' (Matthew 5:48). St Paul describes the Christian life as a 'living sacrifice' (Romans 12:1). The phrase *sola scriptura* illustrates the uniqueness of this form of deontological Christian ethics.

For other Christians, notably **Roman Catholics**, revelation is not confined to the Bible but accessible through the natural world, reason and conscience. **Natural law** was developed by Aquinas and affirmed by the Church in *Veritatis Splendor* (1993). There is much debate about whether natural law in itself is particularly Christian. If natural law is **autonomous** and based on human reason alone, then it is not distinctively religious. Aquinas' version is **heteronomous** as it combines Christian revealed law

(Bible and Church tradition), the primary precept to worship God, the theological virtues (faith, hope and love) as well as reason.

For liberal or **radical Christians**, such as **Joseph Fletcher**, there is only one command and that is to love, but in all other respects ethics are essentially autonomous and **teleological**. His situational approach considered that every situation is judged relatively to the principle of love (or *agape*). The three other 'working principles' that guide moral decision making are: pragmatism, positivism and personalism.

Divine command theory

The question how far Christian ethics may be seen as absolutist or relativist is illustrated by the problem of **divine command**. The dilemma was clearly set out by Plato in the **Euthyphro dilemma**:

(a) Is an act good because God commands it? *or*

(b) Is an act good and God commands it?

In (a), good is absolute because God is all-powerful, all-knowing and all-loving and therefore everything he commands is intrinsically good and must be obeyed. But the problems are: God's commands in the Bible often contradict each other; he appears to command things that are immoral; how can we know what God commands and what might just be our own thoughts?

The alternative is (b), the **weak divine command** theory. This version presents 'good' as something distinct from God that we work out through reason and which God then confirms. This is the view preferred by Fletcher (and Kant). If this is so, good is relative and situational. But the problem with the weak divine command version is that it effectively makes God redundant, or at least secondary to human reason.

1 Why do conservative Christians consider the Bible to be a primary source of deontological revealed ethics?

....

....

....

2 Complete the following biblical passages, which are central to Christian ethics.

God–human covenant relationship: 'You shall have n .... other g .... before me' (Exodus 20:3).

Human–human relationships: 'You shall not k .... You shall not c ....

a .... You shall not s ....' (Exodus 20:13–15).

Social justice: 'But let j .... roll down like waters, and r .... like an

ever flowing s .... ' (Amos 5:24).

Treatment of enemies: 'Love your e .... and p .... for those who

p .... you' (Matthew 5:44).

Love, the central Christian virtue: 'So f .... , h .... and l .... abide,

these three; but the g .... of these is l ....' (1 Corinthians 13:13).

Sanctity of life: 'Then G .... said, "Let us make man in our own i .... ,

after our l .... "' (Genesis 1:26).

3 What is Jesus' 'inner law'? Give examples.

....

....

....

4 Outline two problems of using the Bible as a source of Christian ethics.

....

....

....

5 Why is natural law the basis for Christian ethics for Roman Catholics?

....

....

....

6 Explain why Aquinas' natural law might be considered heteronomous.

....

....

....

....

7 Why does situationism regard Christian ethics as autonomous and teleological?

....

....

....

8 How does situationism steer the middle path between legalism and antinomianism?

....

....

9 Outline Fletcher's four working principles.

....

....

....

....

....

10 Complete the following quotations from Fletcher's book *Situationism*.

Love 'r .... the absolute, it does not a .... the relative!'

Christian ethics means 'deciding to say, "Y .... " to the f ....

assertion that "God is l .... ".'

'The legalist is a *w* .... asker (what does the l .... say?); the situationist is a

w .... asker (who is to be h .... ?).'

11 Divine command theory asserts that, without God, humans cannot know how to be moral. Complete the following statements:

An act is .... if and only if it is .... by God.

If God is .... and .... and .... then

it follows that whatever he commands is good.

12 Plato's Euthyphro dilemma challenges divine command by posing the question:

Does God .... goodness (or holiness) because it is .... or is

it .... because God .... it?

13 Outline two problems of the divine command theory raised by the story of Abraham's near sacrifice of Isaac (Genesis 22:1–19).

....

....

....

....

....

....

14 Outline the weak divine command theory.

....

....

....

....

....

....

15 Give two reasons why the weak divine command theory undermines God.

....

....

....

....

....

....

....

....

....

Exam-style question

Answer the following part questions on a separate sheet of paper. Allow 25 minutes for Part a and 15 minutes for Part b. Use 2 minutes to plan and 2 minutes to reread your essay and correct mistakes.

a Explain divine command theory.   25 marks (25)

b 'Religious ethics must either be deontological or teleological but not both.' Discuss.   10 marks (15)

Topic 6
The right to life and the sanctity of life

Sanctity of life arguments

Many sanctity of life arguments start from the theological premise that, as life is God-given, it is intrinsically worthwhile and valuable and cannot be taken away by others. In the Jewish-Christian biblical tradition, humans are made in the **image of God** (Genesis 1:27) and, as thinking (sentient) beings, share in God's divinity.

For Christians this is expressed in the way in which God reaffirms his relationship with humans in the person of Jesus (John 1:14). To destroy a life is to violate a person's right to existence and **blaspheme** against God. The Old Testament Book of Job states this clearly, 'The Lord gave, and the Lord has taken away' (Job 1:21). It is a fundamental rule of civilised societies that killing should be morally wrong and the sixth of the **Ten Commandments** states 'You shall not murder' (Exodus 20:13); it is therefore a characteristic of the Jewish **covenant** relationship that all life is a blessing and a gift from God, so humans are commanded 'to choose life' (Deuteronomy 30:19).

The sanctity of life principle asserts that respect for people recognises their right to live and our duty as God's stewards (Genesis 1:28) to preserve and protect it. The Christian notion of love not only means to will one's neighbour's good but also to endure suffering (as expressed in the suffering and sacrifice of Christ).

The **weak sanctity of life** argument does not agree that life must be endured at all costs. If life is a gift from God, then it is ours to dispose of as we think fit. Suffering is necessary (to be a 'living sacrifice') to give meaning to life but not when it becomes pointless and agonising. Situational Christian ethics consider that the principle of value is love (agape). It is therefore sometime more humane to allow a person to die, or to die for others (martyrdom). Treating human life as an absolute is a form of idolatry and turns it into a commodity.

The **natural law** tradition adds an important idea to sanctity of life. One of Aquinas' primary precepts is to preserve life, but this does not mean all life, only *innocent* human lives. An innocent life is defined as one that is not deliberately threatening the lives of others. Natural law sanctity of life therefore permits the use of legitimate force (such as war and capital punishment) to take the lives of those who threaten to kill or undermine the stability of society.

Kant's version of the sanctity of life principle establishes the right to life but not the right to take one's own life (i.e. suicide). In his example on suicide he argues that individuals in a great deal of pain cannot out of self-love justify taking their own life. The reason for this is that, first, it cannot be a universal duty for us all to take our lives when in pain and, second, it treats the body as a means to an end (contrary to the law of humanity or practical imperative). Kant, therefore, offers a non-religious version of the sanctity of life principle.

Critics of sanctity of life arguments

Critics of the sanctity of life principle, notably various utilitarians (such as Peter Singer), argue that the strong version of the sanctity of life often has little regard for people as persons because it is more concerned with keeping people alive than with the quality of their existence. They also reject the weak sanctity of life position because it is no more than a confused version of their quality of life position. The quality of life principle takes account of a person's preferences, desires, consciousness and degree of pain/pleasure. These factors do not need to refer to God to make them valid, as the weak sanctity of life position suggests.

1 What is the major distinction between the Christian strong sanctity of life and weak sanctity of life principles?

....

....

....

....

2 The Christian sanctity of life principle illustrates why life is God-given and how it should be treated. Look up the following: John 3:16, Genesis 1:27, Job 1:21, Psalm 139:13, Deuteronomy 30:19, 1 Corinthians 6:19.

Quote biblical texts where human life is described as being holy and set apart by God:

....

....

....

Quote a biblical text that states that the destiny of human life is God's:

....

....

Quote biblical texts that command respect for human life:

....

....

Quote a biblical text that places love as a core value in the treatment of others:

....

....

3 Why does the Catholic *Evangelium Vitae* argue that we live in a 'culture of death'?

....

....

....

4 Why does weak sanctity of life support the notion of 'extraordinary means'?

....

....

....

5 What is Stanley Hauerwas' central weak sanctity of life position based on St Paul's idea of being a 'living sacrifice'?

....

....

....

6 What is vitalism and why is it important for sanctity of life arguments?

7 Outline Aquinas' vitalist position.

8 Give three of Aquinas' primary natural law precepts which reinforce the sanctity of life position.

9 Why does natural law argue that a non-innocent human life should not be protected absolutely?

10 Outline how the natural law doctrine of double effect may permit the death of innocent people.

11 Explain how Kant's categorical imperative and the good will establish a non-religious sanctity of life principle.

12 Explain how Kant's practical imperative and kingdom of ends reject suicide.

13 Complete Kant's question about suicide:

'There only remains the question as to whether this principle of s.................... -l....................

can become a u.................... l.................... of n....................'

14 Why is the right to life considered to be a fundamental right?

....

....

....

15 Give two strengths of the sanctity of life arguments.

....

....

....

....

....

....

....

16 Explain why utilitarians such as Peter Singer and Helga Khuse reject the sanctity of life principle.

....

....

....

....

....

....

....

....

Exam-style question

Answer the following part questions on a separate sheet of paper. Allow 25 minutes for Part a and 15 minutes for Part b. Use 2 minutes to plan and 2 minutes to reread your essay and correct mistakes.

a Explain the religious and non-religious principles of the sanctity of life.　　　　　　　　　　　　　　　　　　**25 marks**　**25**

b 'All human life should be protected absolutely.' Discuss.　　**10 marks**　**15**

Topic 7
Abortion and personhood

Pro-choice and pro-life views

The issue of abortion raises many issues to do with rights, freedoms, the law and the medical profession. Fundamental to all arguments is that 'every child is a wanted child'. **Pro-choice** arguments consider that bringing an unwanted child into the world is unfair; **pro-life** arguments consider that, regardless of external conditions, a baby is intrinsically worthwhile and always wanted.

The law in the UK (Human Fertilisation and Embryology Act, 1990) allows abortion up to 24 weeks into pregnancy where pregnancy threatens the mother's life or her mental or physical well-being. Abortion is permitted at *any time* if the foetus is severely abnormal.

The pro-choice/pro-life distinction relies on whether the embryo is or is not a person. If the embryo is a person, then it becomes morally considerable; if the embryo is not a person, then the moral issues of abortion focus on the autonomy of the mother and others who may be affected.

There are two broad approaches: the **vitalist** believes that, once a human being acquires a soul, it is always considered a person; the **bundle view** believes that personhood comprises various elements including consciousness, reason, sentience, memory, which may develop (and be lost) over time.

According to the **natural law** primary precept of preserving an innocent human life, the foetus/baby must be protected at all times. But the problem is judging at what stage the foetus becomes a person. Aquinas and others placed it at the time when the baby moved — 40 days for boys and 90 for girls. The modern Roman Catholic Church considers it to be at conception, but others argue for implantation or brain activity. The **doctrine of double effect** may justify the unintended *side effect* of a baby's death if a woman's life is threatened by an ectopic pregnancy. This is not abortion but treatment of the woman's health.

For **Kantian ethicists**, once the foetus is regarded as a person, then abortion is wrong as it treats the foetus as a means to an end and therefore dehumanises it. Furthermore, the act of killing an innocent human being cannot be universalised.

For Christians who support the **strong sanctity of life** argument, the Bible supports protection of the foetus from conception (Psalm 139:13) and the general principle of being responsible for all innocent life. The **weak sanctity of life** takes into account the welfare of the mother and her situation. It does not consider abortion to be an intrinsic wrong.

Utilitarian arguments

Utilitarian arguments are not interested in sanctity of life but in **quality of life**. Quality of life largely focuses on the mother and her **autonomy** to decide on her own happiness. Rape, handicap and threats to her life appear to be good **welfare** reasons for abortion. Utilitarians take a bundle view of personhood. The interests of the foetus will therefore depend on whether it is sentient and conscious. **Preference utilitarians** argue that, given the choice between preserving the life of a healthy primate and a handicapped human baby, we should choose the primate because its preferences are greater. **Rule utilitarians** might argue that, if it could be shown that remorse, guilt and physical trauma almost always accompany an abortion, then abortion should be avoided unless there are exceptional circumstances.

1 The 1967 Abortion Act as revised by the 1990 Human Fertilisation and Embryology Act states that therapeutic abortion is permitted in certain circumstances. Complete the following:

threats to woman ....

....

threats to existing children ....

....

the pregnancy is under .... weeks

doctor's conscience ....

....

2 What does the analogy of the 'Ship of Theseus' illustrate about problems of personhood?

....

....

3 Explain Locke's conditions for personhood.

....

....

4 What does Peter Singer argue is the minimal condition for personhood?

....

....

5 Compare the vitalist ('enduring self') and 'bundle' views of personhood.

....

....

6 Explain the 'delayed' or 'progressive' ensoulment view.

....

....

....

7 Why do some people consider the foetus is not even a potential person for 14 days after conception?

....

....

8 Give three possible biological moments when the human foetus could be considered an *actual* human person (say why).

....

....

....

9 A 'hard case' in the abortion debate is defined as having a sufficiently good reason to be an exception to the rule (that abortions are wrong). Explain how the following justify abortion:

rape ....

....

....

handicap ....

....

....

threats to mother's life ....

....

....

10 State one implication of Judith Jarvis Thomson's violinist thought exercise concerning abortion and women's rights.

....

....

11 Outline an act/preference utilitarian argument *for* abortion based on:

mother's interests ....

....

status of the foetus ....

....

ends/means ....

....

long-term consequences ....

....

12 Outline an act/preference utilitarian argument *against* abortion based on:

mother's interests ....

....

status of the foetus ....

....

ends/means ....

....

long-term consequences ....

....

13 Give two reasons why a rule utilitarian might oppose abortion.

....

....

....

....

14 Outline the Roman Catholic natural law arguments against abortion based on:

status of the foetus ....

....

primary precepts ....

....

innocent life ....

....

interior act ....

....

life as pilgrimage ....

....

double effect ....

....

15 Complete the following quotations that support the strong sanctity of life Christian ethical arguments against abortion:

'For you did k .... me together in my m .... womb' (Psalm 139:13)

'If men strive together and h .... a woman with c .... so there is a

m .... and hurt follows then you shall give them l .... for

l ....' (Exodus 21:21, 23)

'When Elizabeth heard the greeting of M ...., the b .... leaped in her

w ....' (Luke 1:41)

16 A weak sanctity of life view of abortion held by the Church of England is that *prima facie*:

....

....

17 Explain why Fletcher's situationist argument considers the legalist (or Roman Catholic) position on abortion shocking.

....

....

18 Outline Fletcher's situationist reasons permitting abortion:

pragmatism ....

....

relativism ....

....

positivism ....

....

personalism ....

....

19 Tick all statements that you think a Kantian ethicist might make concerning abortion. Abortion is:

- [ ] justified if it makes the mother's life happier
- [ ] wrong because it treats the foetus as a means to an end
- [ ] justified because the mother's life is worth more than a potential life (foetus)
- [ ] justified because women must always do what is best for their bodies
- [ ] not justified even if the pregnancy is threatening the mother's life
- [ ] justified as the lesser of two evils

Exam-style question

Answer the following part questions on a separate sheet of paper. Allow 25 minutes for Part a and 15 minutes for Part b. Use 2 minutes to plan and 2 minutes to reread your essay and correct mistakes.

a Explain how the religion you have studied deals with the issue of abortion. **25 marks** (25)

b 'What God commands must be obeyed.' Discuss. **10 marks** (15)

Topic 8
Right to a child and issues of infertility

Ethical arguments about a right to a child

The question of whether a couple have a right to a child depends on what is meant by a 'right'. Some argue for **natural rights** that are God-given or intrinsic, which enable humans to flourish as human beings. Rights are intended to protect the autonomy of individuals. Many reject natural rights (Bentham called them 'nonsense on stilts'), preferring **human rights**, i.e. rights established through agreement to enable human welfare. The question is whether either natural rights or human rights support a couple's right to a child.

Article 16 of The Universal Declaration of Human Rights states: 'Men and women of full age...have the right to marry and found a family.' But do they have an absolute right? Does the article mean only that the state cannot prohibit a couple from having a child? Or does it mean that, if a couple cannot have a child by ordinary means (because of infertility), society has a duty to help them?

Reasons for opposing the right to a child are: being childless is not considered a general welfare issue (and therefore not a right) so society does not have a duty to assist; religious traditions considered a child is a **gift** not a right — it is a blessing of marriage. Even so, **assisted reproduction** may be used as it is no different from treating any other health problem. The causes of **infertility** include: inadequate sperm/eggs; failure to conceive; failure of the fertilised gamete to implant in the uterus; miscarriage.

Assisted reproduction includes: surrogacy, in vitro fertilisation (IVF), egg/sperm/embryo donation. These different processes raise issues such as: the rights of a surrogate mother or donor egg/sperm; the problem of identity of a child conceived using donor sperm/egg; the 'commodification' or treatment of a child as thing or acquisition.

In the **Christian** biblical revealed tradition, the purpose of marriage is to have children but they are a gift not a right (just as all life is a gift from God). Eve says she has given birth to a child (Cain) 'with the help of the Lord' (Genesis 4:1). Use of donors is generally regarded as a form of adultery.

In **natural law**, the primary purpose of sexual intercourse is for procreation. The Roman Catholic view in *Humanae Vitae* (1968) is that nothing should separate **unitive** (loving sex) from **procreative** sex. This means that all forms of assisted reproduction are illicit (unlawful).

For most **utilitarians**, the main concern is the inclusion of donors and people outside the intended parents' relationship. In the case of **surrogacy** there is a danger that the woman who bears the child (the surrogate) for a couple might not wish to give up the child to the commissioning parents. The use of donors (in IVF) could cause long-term problems for the child's sense of **identity**. However, some argue that, as adopted children can form happy families, then by analogy so too can children born from donors.

Kantians argue against couples who desperately desire a child but do so to acquire a commodity not a person (according to the second imperative). They warn that a surrogate mother's body is being treated as a means to an end. Kantianism could support the right to have a child if having a child were seen as essential for the welfare of all humans.

---

1 **Explain the purpose of natural rights and duties (refer to John Locke).**

....

....

2 Explain how human rights are different from natural rights (refer to Bentham).

....
....
....
....

3 How might natural law be the basis of a 'right to a child' argument?

....
....
....
....
....

4 How might Article 16 of *The Universal Declaration of Human Rights* support *and* not support the right to a child?

....
....
....
....
....

5 Many Christians argue that a child is a gift and a blessing, not a right. Psalm 127:3 says:

'Sons are a h .... from the L .... , children are a r .... from him.'

6 Approximately what percentage of couples in the West is infertile (select one)?

☐ 1–5%   ☐ 6–9%   ☐ 10–15%   ☐ 16–20%

7 Assisted reproduction includes (tick all possible):

☐ surrogacy   ☐ in vitro fertilisation

☐ transxenotype transfer   ☐ sperm donation

☐ adoption/fostering   ☐ egg donation

☐ parallel zygote transfer   ☐ embryo donation

8 Define the following in surrogacy:

commissioning/intended parents ....
....

surrogate ....
....

partial surrogacy ....
....

9 A major concern of various forms of IVF is rights and consent of donors. Explain the issues of:

use of aborted foetus eggs ....

....

....

right to know a donor ....

....

....

ownership of frozen embryos ....

....

....

10 Explain why commercial surrogacy is seen as a form of slavery.

....

....

....

11 Complete by filling in the missing words:

The Roman Catholic encyclical H .... V .... (1968) is based on n ....

l .... and argues that AIH is wrong because there must be no division between the

p .... and the u .... aspects of sex. It rejects all use of donors.

However, surrogacy might be possible as set by biblical precedent in the story of Abraham

and H .... Nevertheless, the story illustrates the dangers of surrogacy. It is rejected

because it is an a .... good.

12 The Roman Catholic document *Donum Vitae* (1987) states:

'The g .... of human life must be a .... in m ....

through the specific and exclusive acts of h .... and w ....'

13 Why have some Catholic natural law ethicists rejected IVF and donors as a form of adoption for married couples?

....

....

....

....

14 Explain why Kantians warn that assisted reproduction leads to 'commodification' of the child.

....

....

....

....

15 Explain why many biblical Christian ethicists may accept IVF (AI) but reject the use of donors (AID).

....

....

....

....

16 The Church of England's *Personal Origins* (1996) supports donors in IVF because:

....

....

....

....

17 Outline two reasons why utilitarians might reject IVF.

....

....

....

....

....

....

Exam-style question

Answer the following part questions on a separate sheet of paper. Allow 25 minutes for Part a and 15 minutes for Part b. Use 2 minutes to plan and 2 minutes to reread your essay and correct mistakes.

a Explain why there is ethical disagreement about a couple's right to a child.

25 marks

b 'Any method that enables an infertile couple to have the child they desire is acceptable.' Discuss.

10 marks

Topic 9
Euthanasia and quality of life

What is euthanasia?

As euthanasia is primarily an issue about very sick people, the ethics of euthanasia raise important medical ethical principles about the doctor–patient relationship. The doctor's promise is: 'I will give no deadly medicines to anyone if asked, nor suggest any such counsel' (British Medical Association). Euthanasia means a 'good/merciful death'. There are various forms of euthanasia: one distinction is between active and passive (or direct and indirect) euthanasia.

Active euthanasia usually refers to **voluntary** euthanasia when the patient asks the doctor to end his or her life. In the UK the **1961 Suicide Act** permits suicide but forbids any assistance. Assisted suicide requires *indirect* help from a doctor, but lacks the essential care or **beneficence** of the doctor directly administering euthanasia. **Passive euthanasia** lacks the consent of the patient and is simply murder. In its most extreme form it could refer to genocide ('mercifully' killing a despised racial minority). More often it means **allowing to die**, such as permitting a very sick premature baby to die or removing a life-support system from a 'persistent vegetative state' (PVS) or brain-dead patient (as in the Tony Bland case) thereby allowing him or her to die naturally.

For **utilitarians**, the main concern is the sick person's **quality of life**. This may be judged by using the pain/pleasure principle or QALYs (quality assured life years) but the major problem for the utilitarian is **consent**. Some argue that, although respect for a person's **autonomy** is fundamental to the quality of life argument, a very sick person who requests euthanasia may not be in the right state of mind to give informed consent. A related issue might be that the act or preference utilitarian doctor might kill someone because *they* think it is in the patient's **best interests** to do so but the fear is that this could lead to a slippery slope, non-voluntary, euthanasia. This is where **rule utilitarianism** can set guidelines.

In **natural law**, some doctors support the **doctrine of double effect**. A doctor's duty is to alleviate pain but in some cases pain relief using a very high dose of morphine might *indirectly* kill the patient. This may be justified if the **interior acts** or intentions of the doctor are good. Interior acts are governed by the virtues, especially those of care and trust. Some would argue that, as a **duty of care** to a patient does not mean keeping him or her alive at all costs, then passive euthanasia (i.e. allowing to die) could be justified as good medical practice.

In the revealed **Christian tradition**, as egoistical suicide is regarded as a sin, so is euthanasia. **Augustine** argues that suicide is blasphemous as it: rejects God-given life; acts against the sixth of the Ten Commandments; allows no time for repentance; is cowardly. As euthanasia is a form of assisted suicide, it is rejected for similar reasons. The **weak sanctity of life** Christian may support euthanasia based on love and compassion, using similar situational considerations as the utilitarian.

Kant argues that suicide cannot be a duty — it cannot lead to the summum bonum in the kingdom of ends, as it would destabilise society. Suicide is selfish and cannot be universalised; it also treats the death of the body as a means to an end and so fails to respect the person as an end in him- or herself.

---

1 **Explain the following terms:**

suicide ....

....

....

assisted suicide ....

....

voluntary euthanasia ....

....

non-voluntary euthanasia ....

....

passive euthanasia ....

....

active euthanasia ....

....

2 **Outline what the 1961 Suicide Act states about suicide and assisted suicide.**

....

....

....

....

....

3 **What reasons did Plato and Aristotle give against suicide?**

....

....

....

....

....

4 **David Hume argued (in *Of Suicide*) strongly in favour of autonomy and the right to commit suicide. His reasons are (*complete quotations*):**

'A man who retires from life, does no h .... to society; he only ceases to do

g ....'

'I believe that no man ever t .... away a l .... that was w ....

keeping.'

5 Explain Augustine's traditional Christian arguments against suicide due to:

no right to condemn to death ....

....

lack of courage ....

....

lack of repentance ....

....

blasphemy ....

....

mortal sin ....

....

6 Give two biblical reasons why the Christian strong sanctity of life argument rejects euthanasia.

....

....

....

....

7 Explain how the Christian weak sanctity of life argument may support voluntary euthanasia based on the principles of (a) compassion and (b) life is a gift not a burden.

....

....

....

....

8 Explain how the following natural law primary precepts establish that active euthanasia is intrinsically wrong:

stability of society ....

....

duty to worship God ....

....

duty to uphold ordinary means of life ....

....

protect innocent human life ....

....

9 Explain how the natural law doctrine of double effect may permit passive 'euthanasia' based on the principles of:

primary intention ....

....

proportionate means ....

....

10 Give two reasons why utilitarians reject the double effect justification for passive euthanasia.

....

....

....

....

11 What is a QALY? How is it similar to Bentham's hedonic calculus?

....

....

....

....

....

12 Give one act/preference utilitarian argument for and one rule/welfare utilitarian argument against euthanasia:

for ....

....

against ....

....

13 Give two Kantian reasons against suicide/euthanasia.

....

....

....

....

....

14 Complete this quotation from Kant in his argument against suicide out of self-love:

'One sees at once a c .... in a system of nature whose l ....

would destroy a l .... by means of the very same feeling that a .... so as to

stimulate the f .... of l .... , and hence there could be no existence

as a system of n ....' (*Grounding for the Metaphysics of Morals 1.422*)

15 Explain why some (such as J. S. Mill) consider autonomy to be an important factor in deciding on a person's quality of life and the right to euthanasia.

....

....

....

....

16 Explain why some (such as Jonathan Glover) consider consciousness to be the foundation of determining a person's quality of life and how this might justify euthanasia.

....

....

....

....

17 Explain why some (such as hedonic utilitarians) consider pleasure and absence of pain to be the foundation for determining a person's quality of life.

....

....

....

....

18 Explain the following criticisms of quality of life (QOL) arguments:

QOL dehumanises ....

....

QOL is too subjective ....

....

QOL denies human dignity ....

....

Exam-style question

Answer the following part questions on a separate sheet of paper. Allow 25 minutes for Part a and 15 minutes for Part b. Use 2 minutes to plan and 2 minutes to reread your essay and correct mistakes.

a Explain how the quality of life principle might be applied to the problems surrounding euthanasia. 25 marks

b Assess the view that no one has a right to end their life. 10 marks

Topic 10
Genetic engineering

What is genetic engineering?

Genetic engineering questions to what extent scientists are permitted to 'play God' with the very building blocks of life itself. **Human embryo research** is governed by law (the HFE Act) to permit research on foetal development for up to **14 days**. The reasons for research include: developing different forms of contraception; finding the causes of infertility; detection of genetic abnormalities. This last category poses the question of what kinds of **gene therapies** are morally acceptable.

Genetic engineering on humans falls into two kinds: **negative therapy** — the removal of defects caused by single defective genes (such as the gene that causes cystic fibrosis or Huntington's disease); **positive therapy** — the enhancement (improvement) of the embryo's genes (e.g. sex and skin colour). More scientifically significant is the distinction between **germ-line gene therapy** where alterations to a gene affect *future* generations, and **somatic gene therapy** where the manipulation affects only the *individual*.

Ethical debates

The ethical debates focus on the removal/enhancement distinction. For some ethicists, all gene therapy is enhancement and there should be no restrictions. Others argue that moral lines or boundaries should be set because, if these are not done, the consequences could be disastrous. Gene therapy also raises the moral problem of **screening** the foetus in order to detect genetic defects and how this knowledge should be used (who should know and what actions should take place).

Another area of concern is the use of human **stem cells**. Stem cells are those that have not yet taken on any particular cell function, e.g. as organs, tissues, bone. However, not all stem cells are entirely the same: **embryonic** stem cells (ES) are **totipotent** (i.e. can become any kind of body cell) whereas **adult** stem cells (AS) are **multipotent** (i.e. can become one of a limited range of cells). The ethical issues are: ES cells have to be harvested from embryos (up to 14 days from conception), which means killing them; AS cells can be found in marrow and the umbilical cord but are less predictable and can cause cancers. Stem cells can also be produced through **cloning**. As the cloned stem cell is produced using the *same* DNA as the person having the treatment, there is far less likelihood that the body will reject it.

Genetic engineering is also used in **plants** and **animals**. Plant genes can be manipulated to provide greater yields and be more disease resistant. This is especially important for producing cheap food in large quantities for the world's increasing population. Animals have always been selectively bred for similar reasons. The law also permits **xenotransplantation** and cloning animal gametes with human gametes (hybrids) for research purposes and to provide human tissue.

Kantians consider that genetic engineering appears to be treating the foetus as a **commodity** (as a means to an end) and not as a person in its own right. Kantians may not rule out negative gene therapy because the universal duty of parents must be to give their children the best possible biological start. If the human embryo is regarded as a person, then ES and cloning are wrong, as these treat the embryo as a thing to 'cannibalised' for organ parts. Kantians have no particular duties to plants and animals in themselves unless genetic engineering affects human society.

Natural law might begin by considering to what extent genetic technology leads to a flourishing society. Roman Catholic natural law rejects ES acquired by killing the embryo; negative genetic therapy is acceptable if this does not kill the embryo. But positive gene therapy (enhancement) is rejected as demeaning to human dignity, as is germ-line therapy, because of the risks to future generations.

In the **Christian** biblical revealed tradition, the principle of stewardship supports gene therapy along similar lines to natural law reasoning, providing it maintains human dignity. The use of ES is rejected because life begins at conception (Psalm 139). The liberal **weak sanctity of life** argument may permit ES because the very early embryo is not considered a person. Christians are divided as to whether positive gene therapy is exploiting the world or adding creatively to it.

All **utilitarians** consider the short-/long-term risks of somatic/germ-line engineering. Welfare/preference utilitarians consider the cost-benefits of having healthy or productive future generations of humans and crops/animals. Utilitarians support ES as the early embryo has no preferences. Most regard 'line-drawing' in positive gene therapy as an arbitrary and limiting process.

1 In UK law, what is the upper limit to human embryo research? Why?

2 Give three reasons in favour of embryo research.

3 On what grounds does the Christian strong sanctity of life principle object to *all* embryo research?

4 Give two reasons why a Christian weak sanctity of life argument might support the use of human embryo research.

5 Outline a preference utilitarian (Peter Singer) argument for embryo research.

6 Why do natural law ethicists argue that the very early embryo has an *interest* in not being used in embryo research?

....

....

....

....

7 Why is gene therapy (or genetic engineering) useful in:

plants ....

....

....

....

animals ....

....

....

....

humans ....

....

....

....

....

8 What is the difference between negative and positive gene therapy?

....

....

....

....

9 Give two reasons why positive gene therapy (enhancement) is morally acceptable.

....

....

....

....

10 Give two reasons why positive gene therapy should be resisted.

....

....

....

....

⑪ **Embryonic screening is good because** (*two reasons*):

....

....

....

....

⑫ **Embryonic screening is bad because** (*two reasons*):

....

....

....

....

⑬ **Give two act utilitarian arguments for the use of somatic gene therapy.**

....

....

....

....

⑭ **Why might welfare or preference utilitarians support germ-line gene therapy?**

....

....

....

....

⑮ **Stem cells are very helpful in genetic engineering. Stem cells are** (*tick the correct definition*)**:**

☐   somatic cells that cannot divide or become specialised cell types

☐   somatic cells that can produce only more cells of the same kind

☐   undifferentiated somatic cells that can divide and produce more the same

☐   undifferentiated somatic cells that can divide or become specialised cell types

⑯ **What is the major *moral* objection to the use of embryonic stem cells (ES)?**

....

....

⑰ **What is the main *biological* danger of using adult stem cells (AS)?**

....

....

18 Why does the Roman Catholic natural law position reject the use of ES cells from the very early human embryo (the 'blastocyst') *even* if it has stopped developing?

....

....

....

....

....

19 Why does natural law consider germ-line enhancement to be morally wrong?

....

....

....

....

....

20 Some people advocate animal/human hybrids in genetic engineering. What is the view of:

Utilitarians ....

....

....

Kantians ....

....

....

Christian biblical ....

....

....

Natural law ....

....

....

21 The Christian theologian Paul Ramsey argued in his book *F* ....
M .... that genetic engineering is the 'domination of technology'. This is bad because:

....

....

....

....

....

22 The Christian theologian and scientist Teilhard de Chardin argued in favour of genetic enhancement and human cloning because:

....

....

....

....

23 Explain how the categorical and practical Kantian imperatives reject the use of ES cells.

....

....

....

....

....

....

Exam-style question

Answer the following part questions on a separate sheet of paper. Allow 25 minutes for Part a and 15 minutes for Part b. Use 2 minutes to plan and 2 minutes to reread your essay and correct mistakes.

a Explain the moral issues raised by human embryo research.   25 marks   25

b Assess the view that genetic engineering is wrong because we should not play God.   10 marks   15

TOPIC 11

War and peace

Topic 11
War and peace

Reasons for war

There are many reasons for the use of war — not all are to do with protection of life. Some see war as an **expression** of moral values (war militarism), whereas others see it as a means to an end (war realist) and an instrument of state. The **war realist** argues that, where the state is concerned, the complexities of private morality cannot and should not be transferred wholesale into the public arena. **Michael Walzer's** communitarian war realist argument is influential here, especially his

discussion of when it is right to intervene in another country's war. The just war argument (JWA) argues for continuity between a private morality and the affairs of state. The **pacifist** also argues for the continuity of private and public morality. If violence is wrong at the personal level, then there is no justification for its use in the public sphere. There are two forms of pacifism: absolute and contingent.

Absolute and contingent pacifists

Absolute pacifists (such as **Michael Wink**) regard violence as totally unacceptable as it demeans our view of human dignity and always leads to worse results than non-violence. The best-known Christian absolute pacifists are the **Quakers**, who take Jesus' teaching from the **Sermon on the Mount** ('Blessed are the peacemakers') and reject all forms of war. **Contingent pacifists** argue that, as there is a duty to protect the innocent, then in extreme cases and as a last resort, war is probably the lesser of two evils. Christian contingent pacifists consider Jesus' teaching in the Sermon on the Mount to be a *goal* to achieve perfection but, in an imperfect world, the goal may not always be achievable. **Kant's** essay *Toward Perpetual*

Peace (1795) is an example of non-religious contingent pacifism in which he balanced the categorical imperative (no war) with practical considerations (human nature).

The criticisms of absolute pacifism are that it fails to distinguish the innocent and non-innocent; it can prolong wars by failing to use sufficient means to end them. The most significant criticism is that absolute pacifists fail to acknowledge that an 'omission' (refraining from war/violence) is morally equivalent to an 'act' (war) when innocent people die as a consequence. This is the principle of **acts and omissions**.

Just war argument

The principles of the just war argument (JWA) or just war theory (JWT) may go back to Plato and Aristotle but its form today was developed in Christian circles and the **natural law** tradition — although there is nothing that makes it an *exclusively* Christian argument. Utilitarians, notably **rule utilitarians**, might equally agree with the main elements of the JWA. Aquinas developed Augustine's principle into the first three elements. Others, notably **Francisco de Vitoria**, added the condition of **proportionality** to right intention and **Hugo Grotius** supplied the natural law

principle that the innocent (i.e. non-combatants) should have immunity *in war*. The essential element in the JWA is that the intention is to secure peace. The two elements of JWA are **Jus ad Bellum** (justification for going to war) and **Jus in Bello** (justice in war). Some add a third, which is **Jus post Bellum** (justice after war), sometimes called an 'exit strategy', which considers the aftermath of war and restoration of law and order. The most contested aspect of JWA is whether *all* or just *some of* the conditions have to be met for a war to be just.

1 Distinguish between war realism, war militarism and just war:

realism ....
....
....

militarism ....
....
....

just war ....
....
....

2 Distinguish between absolute pacifism and contingent pacifism:

absolute ....
....
....

contingent ....
....
....

3 Why do some consider there to be a logical difference between the private and public use of lethal force?

....
....
....
....
....

4 'Blessed are the peacemakers.' Give one reason for and one reason against why the Sermon on the Mount supports pacifism.

....
....
....
....

5 Complete the following:

'Non- .... is not an o .... for Christians. It is the e .... of the Gospel.'

(Michael Wink)

6 Outline Tertullian's 'disarming Peter' argument.

....

....

....

7 Why are Quakers absolute pacifists?

....

....

....

....

8 Complete the following:

'We never get rid of an e .... by meeting hate with h ....'

(M .... Luther K ....)

9 Outline why Reinhold Neibuhr argued that absolute pacifism is 'heretical'.

....

....

....

....

10 What error has absolute pacifism committed in its application of 'no killing', according to Anscombe?

....

....

....

....

11 How has absolute pacifism caused wars (according to Anscombe and others)?

....

....

....

....

12 Explain how the absolute pacifist uses the acts and omissions principle as a sufficient condition for not-using-violence.

....

....

....

....

13 What is Singer's utilitarian objection to the pacifist acts and omission defence?

....

....

....

....

14 Outline Kant's argument (in *Toward Perpetual Peace*) for contingent pacifism:

good will/reason ....

....

....

practical imperative ....

....

....

categorical imperative ....

....

....

kingdom of ends/league of nations ....

....

....

15 What does Augustine suggest constitutes the primary purpose of a just war?

....

....

....

16 Aquinas argued that a just war could be justified only (*tick correct views*):

☐ if authorised by the sovereign ruler	☐ to avoid pain
☐ to reclaim land	☐ if authorised by the Church
☐ to seek to correct an injustice	☐ to promote good and avoid evil
☐ to convert heathens to Christianity	

17 In the just war argument/theory, indicate which elements are *Jus ad Bellum* (*mark as A*) and which are *Jus in Bello* (*mark as I*):

☐ just cause

☐ discrimination

☐ protection from attack/self-defence

☐ right intention

☐ rejection of genocide, rape, ethnic cleansing, torture

☐ distinction between combatants and non-combatants

☐ not for revenge

☐ no evil means

☐ not for land acquisition

☐ no weapons whose results cannot be properly gauged

☐ last resort

☐ probability of success

☐ proportionality

☐ death/suffering/damage should be outweighed by benefits

☐ force should be judged by the ends in mind

18 Give two reasons why the JWA is supported by natural law.

....

....

....

....

19 Give two reasons why a rule utilitarian might support the JWA.

....

....

....

....

....

20 Give two reasons why utilitarians (of any kind) might reject the JWA.

....

....

....

....

21 Michael Walzer, a communitarian war realist, argues that morally (*tick true statements*):

☐   war means that politicians have to accept responsibility ('dirty hands')

☐   wars have no rules; the aim is to win

☐   it is wrong to intervene in a war on behalf of another nation

☐   politicians cannot be held morally responsible for war

☐   war places politicians above the law

☐   war does not place politicians above the law

☐   wars have rules; total war is not an option

☐   no one is exempt from blame in war

☐   it is just to intervene in a war on behalf of another nation

22 Complete the following quotations from the Bible. Indicate which ones you think support absolute pacifism, contingent pacifism and war:

'Then they u .... d .... all in the c ....' (Joshua 6:21)

'He looked this way and that, and seeing no one he k .... the E ....

and hid him in the s ....' (Exodus 2:13)

'They shall beat their s .... into p .... , and their spears into

pruning-hooks; nation shall not lift up s .... against n .... , neither shall

they learn w .... any more.' (Micah 4:3)

'Put your s .... back into its place; for all who take the s .... will perish by

the s ....' (Matthew 26:52)

'Blessed are the p .... , for they shall be called s .... of G ....'

(Matthew 5:9)

'But I say to you, Do not r .... one who is e .... But if any one s ....

you on your right c .... , turn to him the o .... also.' (Matthew 5:39)

'You have heard that it was said, "You shall love your n .... and hate your

e .... " But I say to you, L .... your e .... and p .... for those

who persecute you.' (Matthew 5:43–44)

23 How does Luther's two kingdom view support the use of war for many Christians?

....

....

....

....

....

....

....

Exam-style question

Plan your answers to the following part questions in the space provided and then write the answers themselves on a separate sheet of paper. Allow 25 minutes for Part a and 15 minutes for Part b. Use 2 minutes to plan and 2 minutes to reread your essay and correct mistakes.

a Explain the moral reasons for pacifism.　　　　　　　　　**25 marks**　**25**

....

....

....

....

....

....

....

....

....

....

....

....

....

b 'If the just war principles are properly applied there would be no war.' Discuss.

10 marks ⏱ 15

Philip Allan, an imprint of Hodder Education, an Hachette UK company, Market Place, Deddington, Oxfordshire, OX15 0SE

Orders

Bookpoint Ltd, 130 Milton Park, Abingdon, Oxfordshire OX14 4SB
tel: 01235 827827
fax: 01235 400401
e-mail: education@bookpoint.co.uk

Lines are open 9.00 a.m.–5.00 p.m., Monday to Saturday, with a 24-hour message answering service. You can also order through www.hoddereducation.co.uk

© Michael Wilcockson 2014
ISBN 978-1-4718-0010-8
First printed 2014

Impression number   5   4   3   2   1
Year   2019   2018   2017   2016   2015   2014

Printed in Dubai

Hachette UK's policy is to use papers that are natural, renewable and recyclable products and made from wood grown in sustainable forests. The logging and manufacturing processes are expected to conform to the environmental regulations of the country of origin.

P02293

PHILIP ALLAN FOR
HODDER EDUCATION

ISBN 978-1-4718-0010-8

9 781471 800108